Impact Engineering:
Transforming Beyond Agile Project Management

Junade Ali PhD CEng FIET

GW00683757

Written by Dr Junade Ali
Cover design by Katarina Naskovski
Cover photo of Dr Ali by Nicola Bald Photography

ISBN: 978-1-0686057-2-7

Contents

Introduction

Computer software is now an integral part of our homes, financial systems, water treatment plants, power grids, and more. Even so, we still don't understand how to deliver it on-time. According to multiple studies, about 70% of software projects fail to be delivered on-time.

When it comes to project management in general, a study by the accounting firm PwC (PricewaterhouseCoopers) found that only 2.5% of companies successfully complete 100% of their projects.

However, we are even worse when it comes to transformation initiatives. Digital transformation initiatives are undertaken when a company wants to enter the digital era by adopting new technology. The consulting firm McKinsey found that 70% of simple digital transformation initiatives will fail – approximately the same success rate as a terrorist successfully being deradicalized in a program.

The 2018 State of Agile report found that 96% of transformations to adopt the Agile project management methodology will also fail.

In England and Wales, when a company becomes insolvent, it can enter a process known as "administration" whereby control of the business is handed over to a licensed insolvency practitioner in the hope that those creditors who are owed money can be repaid.

Research by Opus Restructuring and Company Watch on over 4,500 companies found that fewer than 10% of companies successfully survive over a five-year span.

These alarming statistics apply not just in the business world, but in our personal lives too.

The US Centers for Disease Control and Prevention found that, in 2018, whilst 55.1% of smokers said they had attempted to quit in the past year, only 7.5% succeeded.

Researchers from King's College London studied a decade's worth of digital health records from 278,982 people. Their September 2015 paper showed the chances of an obese man losing just 5% of their body weight and keeping it off for 5 years is about 1.8%. Only 1 in 1,290 men with severe obesity managed to attain a normal body weight, and, to make matters worse, 78% put the weight back on after five years.

Business and IT novels like The Phoenix Project and The Unicorn Project present a very different picture of success, as if success is a sure-fire strategy if you follow the steps outlined in their books.

The reality, however, is far from what these books portray. I have spent several years working with individuals in a variety of companies who have attempted to achieve these transformation initiatives. I also viewed robust data from these efforts across thousands of teams while I was working for a company which provided the data platform used to measure technical transformation initiatives.

The reality is these transformations were seldom successful, despite being conducted by some of the smartest people around. The individuals driving this change put themselves through emotionally and psychologically draining experiences for ultimate failure.

This research led me to find an alternative model to successfully running transformations – both in the business world and personally – alongside achieving the successful delivery of technical projects on-time and on-budget.

After finishing my PhD, I even went to the University of Cambridge to study cognitive psychology in order to learn the psychological fundamentals described in this book.

Furthermore, I commissioned J.L. Partners to investigate how effective these techniques were in the real-world. The research involved 600 software engineers in the UK and USA: 250 in the UK and 350 in the USA.

Whereas only 35% of projects using the Agile project management techniques were successful, those projects adopting the Impact Engineering methodology described in *this book* saw a 90% success rate – in other words, 8.5 times more likely to succeed than those adopting the requirements engineering practices in the Agile Manifesto.

The UK Parliament's House of Commons Committee of Public Accounts found that £20 billion per year is spent on digital change by the UK Government. Given the high failure rates in such software projects, we can imagine how much money taxpayers could save if the government utilised better software development methodologies. I'll describe these potential savings for businesses in the UK and USA in the chapter on research.

When the transformation components of the book are applied, the effects can be similarly remarkable. For example, from morbid obesity, I've lost 85 kg using these techniques – indeed, about half of which was achieved purely through the psychological approaches described.

I have also seen these techniques be successfully used in real-world business settings and in others personal transformations.

I have long enjoyed reading the business transformation novels of the past, including the works of Eliyahu Goldratt and Patrick Lencioni. While I have somewhat condemned more recent books like The Phoenix Project and The Unicorn Project, I do want to present an alternative model in a similar format.

Therefore, the bulk of this book will tell the story as a business novel. This also gives me the opportunity to talk about real-world case-studies I've encountered while anonymising the details.

In the penultimate chapter before the conclusion, I will share an overview of the scientific research that the book is built upon. The conclusion will outline the key findings, followed by a brief summary of all the techniques used.

The novel component of this book that follows is set "in the present day", meaning May 2024, at the time of writing.

Although the characters depicted here are fictional, the case studies are often based on real-life examples I encountered during my work. I also reference real-world scientific research as I write.

Of course, as I am a software engineer and computer scientist (and although this book has been edited by someone with knowledge of such matters), any psychological or medical information is presented through the lens of a curious computer scientist rather than a healthcare professional. Do not rely on this book for healthcare information and seek professional help in relation to any of the issues mentioned.

I hope you enjoy the following chapters, and I'll return to the first-person at the end of the book.

Willpower

Daniel was returning to his hotel room.

Having endured the long journey from London to Sydney, he had done his best to stay awake all day to offset the effects of jetlag.

Glancing at his phone, he saw a text message from a woman named Jess: "I'm at the bar if you want to catch up?"

Daniel typed out a reply: "Sure, I'll be there in a few minutes."

Entering the hotel, he asked the bell woman for directions to bar. Known as "directors of chaos", the bell women of the QT Hotel in Sydney dress in all-black leather with red hair, fitting for the gothic surroundings of the State Theatre building where the hotel is located.

Entering the bar, he was flagged down by a woman with black hair, aged in her mid-thirties, sat at one of the tables. He took the seat opposite her and no sooner had a waiter approached the table. "Another drink, Dr Jones?"

Jess replied in an Australian accent, "Sure, I'll take another of the same."

The waiter turned to Daniel and said, "And for you, sir?"

Daniel replied, "I'll take a double rum and Coke, please."

As the waiter finished writing on his pad and stepped away, Jess turned to Daniel. "Long flight?"

"Yeah, I went via Los Angeles, so it took over 32 hours," Daniel replied. "You're lucky you just had to come from Melbourne."

Daniel had just turned 31 and had been a software engineer for around 10 years. He had recently found himself promoted into his first engineering management position.

He had first met Jess Jones when he was in the final year of his undergraduate computer science degree, where Jess, a PhD student at the time, was helping him with his undergraduate project.

Whilst Dr Jones was an electrical engineer by training and went to the UK to study for her PhD, she later returned to Melbourne, Australia to study and research organisational psychology.

The waiter quickly returned and placed a glass bottle of a Coca Cola in front of Daniel, with a tall glass filled with a double measure of dark rum and ice.

Daniel looked up at Jess and said, "So this project I'm here to work on, what exactly is it about?"

Jess's eyes focussed on the bottle of Coca Cola in front of Daniel and said, "Dan, in that bottle of Coke, what are the substances which trigger your brain to release dopamine, the pleasure chemical?"

Daniel also looked quizzically at the bottle and replied: "Well, I guess there's sugar and caffeine in there. And when I mix it with the rum, we have alcohol too."

Jess replied: "Exactly. When the recipe for the drink was originally invented, it didn't just contain alcohol, it also contained another substance: cocaine."

Jess continued, "The inventor, John Pemberton, became an opioid addict after he was injured fighting for the confederates in the US civil war, so he invented the drink to replace his morphine addiction. As his addiction got worse, he became ill and nearly bankrupt, so sold the recipe to a company in Atlanta."

Daniel asked, "So what does this have to do with the project? Or are you telling me to drink less Coke?"

Daniel proceeded to mix the cola with the rum and take a sip from the glass.

Jess let out a breathy laugh as she leaned back and took a sip of her own drink: "No, but this goes to the very heart of the topic I'm researching."

Jess went on to say, "Addiction still happens in society, but now we have very powerful tools to help people overcome it. Not only do we have advances in medical science and psychology, but we have medication which can reduce alcohol cravings."

Jess continued: "The same is true with smoking. In the US, half of smokers try to quit every year but only 7.5% succeed."

"So what you're saying is that addiction is hard to overcome?" Daniel questioned. "That hardly seems profound."

"No, this is far more profound than that," Jess replied. "Let's take a look at something else; there are differences in the brain pathways responsible for obesity than to drug addiction, and the influence of genes on obesity is as high as 80%. Yet, despite all the ill-effects of obesity, the chances of an obese man losing just 5% of their body weight and keeping it off for 5-years is about 1.8%."

"Yes, but do we have the same tools to treat obesity?"

"We have some of the most powerful tools that exist," Jess said emphatically. "In the old days, we used to use gastric bands to try and make people full quicker, but there are even better technologies now. Nowadays, we have powerful surgeries that alter the hormones in the body, and we see 90% success rates in treating obesity."

Daniel looked at Jess quizzically and asked, "What do you mean 'alter the hormones'?"

"One procedure that is used is the sleeve gastrectomy – in that procedure we remove part of the stomach that produced ghrelin, a hunger hormone. Patients typically lose up to 70% of their excess body weight after these procedures. We now also have non-surgical approaches like medication originally invented for diabetes becoming available."

"Okay," Daniel sighed, "but still, surgery is expensive, and medication is in short supply. Plus, how safe can it be to operate on the morbidly obese?"

"Well, the surgery is safer than someone having their gallbladder taken out, and if they're type 2 diabetic and had a gastric bypass procedure, chances are they'd go home the next day off all their medication before they've lost any weight," Jess answered

Daniel asked, "So what, you're saying is this is an education problem?"

"Maybe partially," Jess replied, "but even where people want treatment and understand the risks, there is still a hesitancy to receive treatment – people are scared."

Daniel was tired, and the effects of the alcohol were beginning to kick in. He was starting to regret ordering a double measure of rum.

Looking at his glass on the black table, he slowly said, "Okay Jess, so this is a problem which affects people with addiction and obesity?"

Jess replied, "Yes, but it affects all of us. It affects you at work right now."

Daniel was even more confused. "How?"

"In the UK, when a company becomes insolvent and enters administration, it has just a 10% chance of surviving," Jess began. "And by the way, in software engineering we see as many as 96% of transformations to the Agile project management methodology fail. Frankly, you'd have more success deradicalizing a terrorist."

Daniel flagged down their waiter and asked for the bill.

Sensing his tiredness, Jess said: "So clearly, there's a big need for us to understand the psychology behind why transformations fail, both at a personal and business level. This is what I've been commissioned to study by Red Phoenix, the global technology consultancy."

Jess finished her drink and said, "I need a computer system so we can collect the data as we run these studies. The software development project went completely off the rails. When we were taking bids for someone to develop the system, your company was keen and with things looking bleak for the old team, the time is coming for a new team to step in."

Jess pulled a red Mount Blanc pen from her handbag and wrote her name and room number on the bill and signed it.

As Daniel began to protest, she looked up and said: "No worries, you can get coffee tomorrow. Let's catch up after the meeting."

After Jess left, Daniel took a moment to consider everything he had heard. Deciding he was too tired to process it all that night, he made his way up to his own hotel room.

Exhausted from the travel, he unbuttoned the top button on his shirt and fell asleep the moment his head touched the pillow.

Failure

The next day, Daniel left his hotel room and made his way to a nondescript office in the city.

Upon entering the boardroom, a man with an Australian accent stood up and stretched out his hand, saying "Hi, you must be Daniel. I'm Vu, the CEO of Red Phoenix."

"CEO?" Daniel replied. "I'd have thought you'd have more pressing things than coming to a meeting like this."

Vu replied: "Nonsense, this is a critical project, and as you'll find out, there may be some drastic action needed to save this project."

The room filled with employees from Red Phoenix while Jess arrived. The last to arrive were two other attendees wearing guest badges.

Vu said from his seat: "Thank you all for attending, particularly those of you who have travelled from afar to be here. Mike and Brad are here from the team at Flaxseed Software, and I hope we'll be finally hearing about some positive progress with getting the development environment up and running?"

Mike introduced himself: "Hi everyone, I'm Mike, the VP of Engineering at Flaxseed and we're the software development team for Project Renegade based in Reading, England."

Mike continued: "As you know, we work in two-week iterations known as sprints and the team tell me they met with Jess at the last kick-off meeting to discuss what we'd work on. This has now gone through QA and is live in the development environment."

Mike started sharing the screen from his laptop to the television in the meeting room. He said: "As you can see here, the system is live and ready for Jess and her research team to start acceptance testing."

Vu looked to Jess and said, "Jess, do you have everything you need then?"

Jess looked at Vu. "I'm sorry, but no, frankly, I don't. The demo environment went live a few hours ago and there are some significant problems."

Jess looked down at her notebook and started to read. "Firstly, I tried inputting some test data and the scientific calculations are just wrong. It's like whack-a-mole. Every time I raise a problem a bandage is applied."

Jess went on: "Secondly, the most critical functionality we need simply isn't there. The data anonymisation feature is essential for us to even start work."

Vu looked at Mike and said, "Mike, let's start with the data anonymisation feature – I asked you myself three months ago to prioritise that."

Mike looked down at his fingernails. "Well, as you know," he said, "our technology was built upon a scientific research system we devised in house, the architecture of the system now makes adding this functionality quite difficult."

"It's a common feature in any similar platform – why wasn't it there from the outset?" Jess asked.

"We are disrupting this industry," Mike stated. "We are building a new vision based on the capabilities of new technologies like Artificial Intelligence and NudgeTech. We built this technology from the ground up with a microservices architecture, which provides us several key benefits."

Jess replied, "I may be an electrical engineer by training, but I have no interest in your buzzwords – I care about solving the problems."

Vu looked up and spoke to Brad this time. "Brad, you're the CEO of Flaxseed. From one CEO to another, can you not see the predicament these repeated failures put us in?"

"We're a large company," Vu continued, "but every month our key competitor creates a new Red Phoenix in revenue, and they have an entire pharmaceutical arm to generate the money they need to compete with us."

"Every day we're not running these experiments, is another day one of the key problems facing society isn't addressed and we're not delivering an impact," Jess added.

Brad said, "Well, as you know we have a wide variety of customers and the needs of our solution have more than accommodated their needs."

Vu snorted and responded: "Brad, we do our due diligence before entering such procurement decisions. We know your company is losing tens of millions of pounds per year and we are your largest customer. The work you do for your other two customers is completely bespoke."

Looking seriously at Brad, Vu said, "You raised money from venture capitalists on the basis of buzzwords. We want to help you turn that into a real product that solves real-world problems, but you need to let us help you. Either you need to fix the problems or quit the project."

"I'm sorry, yes, the project is late, but we are fully intent on fulfilling our obligations under the contract," Brad replied.

Mike chimed in: "We use the industry-standard Scrum form of Agile to deliver business value. Yes, our project is late, but so are 70% of other projects in the industry. You won't do much better by switching."

"Our developer productivity statistics are phenomenal," Mike concluded. "We are able to deploy code to production in minutes, our developers have high workplace satisfaction scores, and our deployment automation means we rarely have to rollback changes."

Vu said, "The goal of this project is not to deploy code to production as quickly as possible; it is to deliver the software Jess and her team need to run this large-scale scientific work."

Vu moved his mug filled with cold coffee to the side and rested his hands on the table. "I do, however, agree with you on one thing. The chances are, if we outsource to another supplier, the project will fail. You might notice Daniel is attending this meeting. He's here from N. X. T. Systems."

Vu explained: "N. X. T. Systems also bid for this contact and so I asked them to fly in one of their engineering managers to join us, in case we need to hand this project over. I want to give you one last chance here though. You have four weeks to deliver a new, simple product, which matches our needs provided in our requirements document – can you do that?"

"I have already committed my team to using the existing technical architecture and technologies," Mike said. "We are an Agile team; we prefer customer collaboration over working from requirements. I am the software development expert in this room, and that's how we will deliver this project."

"Fine," Vu said. "Effective immediately, we are terminating this arrangement as you are in breach of contract. Our lawyers will email a termination letter over to you in due course. As a gesture of goodwill, we'll cover the costs of the trip you've made here today."

Vu turned to Daniel and said, "Daniel, I will be emailing over to your head office our formal acceptance of the offer that N. X. T. Systems has made to develop this software. Please spend the coming days to gain as much context as possible from Jess."

Narcissism and Loss Aversion

Daniel was reeling by the end of the meeting and retreated to a nearby coffee shop.

The scorching heat didn't warrant a warm drink, so he ordered a cold brew and an iced mocha for Jess.

Jess arrived shortly afterwards and took the seat opposite him, taking a sip of her drink.

"I'm confused," Daniel said. "What happened there?"

"The project had been limping along like this for nearly 9 months," Jess replied. "I'm glad they're finally out of their misery and we can get on and build this."

Daniel took a sip from his own coffee and said, "But Flaxseed Software ... now they'll surely go bankrupt. Why didn't they just take the lifeline?"

Daniel paused for thought and looked quizzically at Jess, finally saying, "Yesterday, you told me how we have powerful tools to address problems like obesity – yet it remains a problem in society. Is this another case like that?"

Jess giggled to herself and said: "Yes, good – the jetlag is finally starting to wear off. Obese patients will struggle to lose weight because they become resistant to leptin, the hormone which tells people to stop eating. As gastric sleeve surgery removes the part of the stomach produces the hunger hormone, ghrelin, while also addressing the leptin resistance issue, we see profound weight loss."

Jess paused to take a sip of her coffee and added, "However, we do also see profound psychological effects that cause people to resist change in all walks of life."

Turning to Daniel she asked, "I don't mean to scare you before you fly home, but if something happened on your flight, do you think you'd act to save yourself?"

Daniel quickly responded: "Of course."

Jess unlocked her iPhone and, after some internet searching, pulled up a black and white photo of a destroyed aircraft on a runway.

Jess said, "This is the Tenerife airport disaster of 1977 where two planes collided with each other. In aircraft disaster movies everyone is screaming and panicking in a disaster, the truth is for 70% of people they will act like nothing is going wrong in a crisis. About another 10% to 15% of people will freak out, but only the remainder will calmly act to save themselves and others. This happened to the passengers during this disaster."

As Jess paused to put her phone down and take another sip of her coffee, Daniel asked, "So that explains why transformations are so difficult to achieve?"

Looking at Daniel's full coffee cup, she remarked, "By the way, don't let your coffee get warm," before continuing: "To an extent, but even in this disaster we see another powerful psychological bias at play. You see, one of the aircraft took off without permission in foggy conditions. Clearly an irrational decision, but the captain would have faced consequences to his reputation and cost issues for the airline if the flight was delayed."

Jess went on: "Loss aversion is part of prospect theory. Prospect theory explains that individuals are more likely to engage in riskier behaviours to prevent losses than to achieve gains. Often, to avoid the repercussions of a loss, people may choose to be dishonest. They might conceal a minor, unintended error rather than face the potential penalties for their actions. For example, for some individuals, the pain from losing $1,000 could only be compensated by the pleasure of earning $2,000."

"This concept was expertly illustrated by Derren Brown in his Netflix special *The Push*," Jess continued, "which attempts to use an escalation of commitment from someone engaging in a minor unethical act to coercing them into committing what they believe to be murder."

"That's interesting," Daniel said, "but surely there can't be many other psychological biases like this?"

Jess chortled. "If only! There's many more. Take the bystander effect, for example. People will walk past someone in crisis rather than help when they're in the presence of others who are doing nothing."

Jess continued: "Dr Anna Lembke, in her book called 'Dopamine Nation', also explains the concept of the pain-pleasure balance. The more pleasure you feel, the easier it is for you to feel pain and the harder it becomes for you to feel pleasure. This can often mean that people in privileged positions like tech workers make it hard to forgo easy pleasure for doing the hard things."

"Or take confirmation bias," Jess went on, "where people won't change their opinions after they have made their minds up. An interesting 2018 study from University College London found those with radical political beliefs exhibit a failure in metacognition, the ability to think about thinking; they were less able to update the confidence in their judgements in light of contradictory evidence."

"How does this explain the way Mike behaved though? Walking away from the project?" Daniel wondered aloud.

"So, I worked with Mike during this project," Jess replied. "One thing I do respect about him is he does set boundaries. In the past I've coached people who find themselves in the same toxic work environments and relationships because they leave one environment, don't set their boundaries, ignore warning signs and then enter into another crisis. When in a new workplace or relationship, they continue to not set boundaries and they get taken advantage of until things boil over. Mike does have some weaknesses too though."

Jess paused to take a sip of coffee and continued: "Mike doesn't have much of a track record of his own achievements, but he definitely has a grandiose sense of self-importance. He exaggerates his achievements and expects to be recognised as superior without actually having the achievements for that recognition. I sometimes wonder if he has narcissistic personality disorder. He's arrogant and haughty a lot of the time."

Jess started searching on her phone as she said, "There is lots of other research showing that software engineers tend to have inflated senses of self-achievement. Take a look at this study done by Engprax and Survation."

Daniel began reading Jess's phone screen. On it was a study showing that 94% of software engineers rate their job performance as average or above. The study also showed that men are 26% more likely than women to consider themselves better than average performers. The researchers pointed to a previous study that was consistent with these findings, with up to 42% of software engineers rating themselves in the top 5% of performers.

As Daniel finished reading, Jess concluded, "Of course, Mike was a special case here, but it's worth bearing in mind how ego affects large populations of people, not just those labelled with a disorder."

"So what you're saying is Mike's ego wouldn't let him fix the problems," Daniel mused as Jess finished her coffee. "And for Brad, the CEO, presumably given the amount of venture capital money he has raised, loss aversion means he's too frightened to take the decisions to allow the business to succeed. Like an ostrich with his head in the sand?"

"Yes, sadly that appears to have been the case here," Jess said. "We like to pretend that software engineering is some wholly rational field, but humans are emotionally driven. There was an interesting study in 2022 by the auditors Ernst & Young and the University of Oxford's business school which found that leaders who prioritise workforce emotions are 260% more likely to be successful in digital transformations. The study found underperforming transformations can increase the emotional strain on the workforce by 136%."

Daniel looked down at Jess's empty coffee cup and said, "Can I get you another? We still haven't discussed what I'm going to do with this new project."

Jess looked at Daniel and said, "I'm afraid I have to go, and after my experience of trying to help Mike and Brad, I'm not keen to prescribe any solutions – I would like you to come to the answers yourself."

"Earlier you said the research said that 70% of software projects fail to be delivered on-time," Daniel responded, "so how am I meant to overcome these odds myself?"

"Yes, 70% of software projects do fail to be delivered on-time, but most transformations fail too – I want you to find the answers yourself. Perhaps start by understanding why software projects fail and that might help you understand where things go wrong."

As Jess left, Daniel's head felt filled with more questions than before he'd arrived.

Defining the Problem

Daniel was onboard Virgin Australia flight 8000 from Sydney to Los Angeles, and the plane was about two hours from landing.

He was thinking about what Jess had told him to research: software project failures. He had taken out his laptop and connected to the in-flight Wi-Fi.

Maybe, he thought to himself, *software projects were failing to be delivered on-time because the quality assurance (QA) processes weren't fit for purpose and there wasn't enough testing. After all, it was very common for software engineers to blame a lack of testing for problems.*

However, thinking about projects he'd been part of in the past, the problems seemed far deeper than testing. Additionally, in the recent Horizon IT Scandal, where faulty Post Office software led to the largest miscarriage of justice in British history, Fujitsu did have quality assurance teams.

He opened Google and reached a Wikipedia article listing software failures and their reasons, but not one of the entries in the 'problems' column listed any issues with testing. Many instead seemed to attribute the issues to 'scope creep' and 'cost overruns'.

The flight attendant came by his seat and said: "Sir, what can I get you from the menu?"

Putting on a smile, Daniel begrudgingly closed his laptop, smiled to the flight attendant and ordered his in-flight meal.

Daniel thought to himself: *Software engineers will often blame testing when things go wrong, but is that actually the reason things do go wrong?*

As he was eating, he thought back to a class he'd taken at university where he had studied "embedded systems", computers which are embedded into every aspect of modern life – from aircrafts to television remotes.

During his class, he remembered studying catastrophic software failures in aircraft and cars. For one of his projects, he had reviewed many incident reports from fatal computer accidents. The root cause of these failures would commonly be attributed to "design issues" rather than software or testing issues.

In the case of a faulty radiation device known as Therac-25, a US government reviewer criticised the lack of a documented specification detailing how the software was designed.

This has been the case in even more recent aviation disasters; Qantas flight 72 saw two military-trained pilots manage to save their aircraft from doom after a previously unknown software design limitation put the Airbus A330 aircraft into a 'death dive'. Fortunately, the issue was investigated and addressed promptly.

However, Daniel couldn't help but think to himself about the message that was hammered into him, that a key principle of Agile software development is "working software over comprehensive documentation".

Two other principles of the Agile Manifesto were "customer collaboration over contract negotiation" and "responding to change over following a plan".

Daniel mused that this seemed at odds with the case studies listed online of the many software projects that had failed due to cost overruns and scope creep.

We are taught to take a dogmatic view of Agile, Daniel thought to himself, *but what if it is not universally good?*

While Daniel had mindlessly eaten his meal lost in thought, the flight attendant returned to collect his tray.

Opening up his laptop again, he realised his next destination was to check to see what had happened as Agile software engineering practices had been adopted.

After Daniel entered the world of work, he was coached in learning Agile by a senior employee who had spent many years working in Japanese automotive engineering. Japan is the spiritual birthplace of Agile software development, where the Toyota Production System was developed to develop cars on a factory line.

When researching how this translated into software, Daniel had found that after unintended car acceleration issues led to numerous fatalities. During a court case following one such death, a software expert pointed to internal communication in Toyota, saying, "In truth, technology such as failsafe is not part of the Toyota Engineering division's DNA".

Okay, Daniel thought to himself, *software isn't like a production line – let's instead look at the earliest cases of where Agile software development was actually used.*

After more searching, he quickly realised that one of the earliest cases of using an Agile software development methodology was in the Post Office

Horizon IT system, the very computer system that had led to miscarriages of justice, including the imprisonment of a pregnant mother. After the problems emerged, the Post Office chose instead to cover these events up, presumably due to the cognitive biases like loss aversion that Jess had told him about.

But Daniel couldn't help but wonder if Agile was actually the root cause of the issue. He went online to the website of the public inquiry of the scandal and started searching documents.

The witness statements described that a methodology known as "Rapid Application Development" was used, a precursor to more modern Agile development methodologies like Extreme Programming and Scrum.

Daniel read that the ongoing public inquiry in the scandal had seen the lack of concrete requirements become a recurring theme in the evidence it heard. This was rooted in the use of the then pioneering Agile methodology used.

One witness, Terence Austin, remarked, "One of the reasons why this got into this situation is that we were forced to do rapid application development and, by doing that, you haven't got a functional specification".

David McDonnell, a former Fujitsu engineering manager – and one of the first internal whistleblowers of the issues – said in his evidence to the Horizon IT Inquiry, "Well, a project such as that – well, any kind of software development project, there should be a framework of how the team work. It should start with the design documents. That's the target of what you are trying to deliver; that's what you are building against."

McDonnell went on: "I know that there had been some documents that were reverse engineered, but they were irrelevant and out of date, and they weren't even in the building when I got there. I had to ask for them."

Daniel was in disbelief; was the fundamental methodology that had been taught to him – enthusiastically prophesised as genius – in fact killing people?

The fasten seatbelt light illuminated and Daniel stowed his laptop for landing.

Predictability

Daniel was meant to connect straight from his flight from Sydney, on to his flight to London from Los Angeles. However, Daniel spotted an opportunity that was too good to miss.

The overbooked connecting flight had been looking for volunteers to delay their flights from Friday to Saturday in exchange for some air miles.

Not only was Daniel happy to take the air miles, but a few of his friends who worked in Silicon Valley, in the north of California, happened to come down to Los Angeles that weekend.

Sleep deprived, Daniel left the airport. Outside, his friend Jacob was waiting for him.

"Hey, long time no see," Jacob said.

"It's been a while, how've you been?" Daniel replied.

"Not bad, not bad," Jacob answered. "Currently working on this start-up – we're working on a developer product. Come on, let's get in the car and chat as we drive."

In the electric vehicle, Jacob began to explain how he was running a start-up to reduce burnout for software engineers.

"Burnout is a massive issue, but we're constantly told we need to iterate faster to meet customer needs quicker," Daniel reflected.

"You see – that opinion is changing around here," Jacob explained. "Lots of companies in the Bay Area spent a ton of time trying to come up with productivity metrics for developers, when in fact what matters is delivery."

"Yes, but how do you achieve delivery faster without working faster?" Daniel asked.

"Well, here's the thing," Jacob replied. "A company called Haystack put out some research they conducted. 90% of US business leaders report on-time delivery as the key factor in evaluating software engineering performance and 89% are concerned with on-time delivery of software projects in their organisations. They studied the UK too and the results are pretty similar."

Jacob continued: "There's been some previous research that has shown that software developers themselves feel pretty similar about the need to deliver software on-time."

"So software needs to be delivered on-time, so people need to work faster?" Daniel quipped back.

Jacob replied, "Here's the thing – we've learnt that 'on-time' means something very different to 'quickly'. This is about predictability not speed. See, I've got a print-out of the study in my glove box, take a read."

Daniel took a look at the study and read: "98% in the UK and 96% in the USA agree with the statement 'The goal of a software engineering team is to deliver high-quality software on-time'".

They stopped at an In-N-Out Burger just off a freeway. Daniel looked at Jacob and said, "You see, I'm becoming sceptical about this Agile stuff. I looked at case studies and they all seem to indicate that actually it's really important to get the requirements and design of a system right before you start building it."

Jacob replied, "I'll be frank with you here, I was always taken aback how bad the specification documents produced in UK tech companies were, here it's common for us to design before we start producing – we did it even when Agile was the hype. Take a look."

Jacob pulled out a laptop from the back seat of his car and showed Daniel the internal documentation system of his start-up.

"For us to find product-market fit with our start-up, our investors have told us it's really important to talk with prospects and customers," Jacob said. "We log that all down here."

Jacob continued: "And when we build, we do it like we were all used to – we write specification documents outlining the customer's needs, the problem, and how we look to solve it. When we do that, the solution just drops out."

Daniel replied: "You see, our company has gone all in on Agile – when we have a new business need, it's logged in a ticket and maybe the engineer working on it will write up what it does in a test plan before it goes live. We don't really collect requirements properly even for the big stuff. I don't know why half the stuff we build is built. We get it wrong a lot, but then we just redo it until it works."

Jacob sniggered and replied, "You just beat it into submission. Come on, let's get some food."

Finding Solutions

Daniel was back in his office and briefing his team on the new project they were to take on.

Paul, the team's Product Manager, looked at Dave and said, "Alright, well, let's start building."

"Hold on Paul," Daniel replied. "I've been thinking about this. You know the last project we worked on, where the customer was never happy with what we produced?"

"Yeah, they kept wanting changes until our architecture could no longer cope with the changes?"

"I've been doing some thinking," Daniel said. "This time, why don't we properly document what the customer needs first before we start building? That means we architect in a way that works towards the solution."

Daniel proceeded to explain his thinking and the discussions he had in California with Jacob.

Paul thought about it and said, "Daniel, I see where you're coming from – I'd be lying if I didn't say that is a problem working at this company. The problem is, though, this is the way we've always done this and it's not the way I was trained on that Agile training course I took."

"Let's just treat it as an experiment," Daniel probed. "If it goes wrong, I'll take responsibility – but if it goes right, we have a huge opportunity here. It'll just take a few hours for either of us to write-up the requirements, maybe a bit of design time, and then we can get one of the engineers to do a specification."

Paul said, "Okay – this does seem a little old-school though. I remember learning waterfall project management back when I was in the army."

"I'm not saying we need to build things differently," Daniel replied. "All I'm saying is that we get these requirements down right."

Later that day, Paul and Daniel were in a meeting room together discussing the requirements.

"So what do we document as requirements? Do we need all the technology wizardry documented?" Paul asked.

Daniel thought for a second and said, "Well, what is the goal of the software we're building?"

"It's to meet the customer's objective – having somewhere that data can be reported from the scientific studies and analysed," Paul replied.

Daniel said, "So would you say the goal is to meet those customer requirements, or for us to deliver our work in a specific technical way?"

"Well, I've been saying for years we need to be more customer-centric and meet the customer requirements, but we do have other requirements too," Paul replied. "We can't be down for a certain amount of time or we need to give them Service Level Agreement refunds, and there's other stuff stipulated in the contract."

"So yes," Daniel replied, "we have customer requirements, but there are both functional requirements and non-functional requirements. There's what the customer needs to be able to use, but they also rely on other stuff to be there too."

"Okay Dan, let me work on this and collect these requirements. What do we do after it's done?" Paul inquired.

"Well, then we can give it to an engineer to turn into a technical specification as to how we actually build it," replied Daniel.

Daniel left the meeting room and went to meet Mo, a software engineer on his team.

"Hey Mo," Daniel said as he approached his desk. "So this new project … would you be open to doing the specification?"

"Sure, just the usual one-page document with some high-level bits?" Mo replied.

"Not this time. I want you to consider the requirements Paul is actually getting down and how to create a solution that will solve those needs. Our current one-pager doesn't really do that, it just shares that we're working on a new project with random technical details. We need to think about it in a systematic way."

Mo began searching for something on his computer and said, "Ah, I've heard about something similar to this. Have you heard of Tokeneer?"

"No, what is that?"

Mo replied: "This was a highly reliable computer system which was made by Altran UK for the US National Security Agency. They produced the software pretty fast, but they did so without having any major defects in the code."

"How did they achieve that?" Daniel asked.

"Well," Mo replied, "they used a requirements analysis process, then they wrote a specification which could be mathematically checked before they actually implemented the code and tested it. They wrote the code in the SPARK Ada language, so they could mathematically check the code worked."

"Well, I don't think we need that level of assurance, but I think that's essentially the high-level process we're looking at. It's essentially a software development lifecycle, or like any other traditional engineering process," Daniel said.

Mo said, "Okay, so what we do is we analyse the requirements, then document that in a specification which we can use for writing the implementation and the automated tests."

Mo looked happily up from his computer screen. Daniel wasn't used to seeing this.

"You know, I'm finally happy we get to do something right the first time instead of squabble with the customer about it afterwards," Mo said.

As Daniel walked away, he smiled and said, "Me too, Mo."

Work-in-Progress

A few days later, Paul and Daniel were in a meeting room looking up at a television screen. They were together reviewing the backlog of work that the team had to work through and trying to prioritise it.

Having adopted an Agile software development approach, the team would work in two-week intervals known as sprints. After this, they would review what was done, reprioritise work, and start a new sprint.

During the sprint, Paul and Daniel would sit down together to review the backlog of work to ensure it was kept manageable, a process known as backlog grooming.

"You know, I've been thinking," Paul said. "When Mo finishes his spec document, how are we going to manage this project?"

"How do you mean?" Daniel replied.

Paul said, "Well, we ditched some of the Agile thinking by doing this specification. What of the rest of the software development flow? Anything else we need to change?"

Daniel thought about what Paul was saying for a few moments. Before he had taken on the team, the team struggled to get any work over the line at all.

Agile projects are often visualised using a Kanban board, in which there were columns representing work to be done, work-in-progress, and work completed. The work would be represented as a card that would move from lane to lane.

The board on Daniel's team was represented on the computer screen which he and Paul were looking at.

Every week, Daniel's predecessor would add more work to the board while last week's work would still be in progress. This meant more work would be in progress, but it would never quite get over the line. It would always be 80% done.

Every morning the team would join their daily "stand-up" meetings to say what they were doing that day, but no one really seemed to have any shared understanding of what was being worked on. Engineers would switch between tasks repeatedly, but every week there would be more tasks to switch between.

Daniel's predecessor was keen never to "waste" any resources and so kept the team busy whether their work was productive or not.

User interfaces would be built far in advance of any backend code for them to interact with. Work would pile up for the software tester to review but would never actually cross the line to completion. In fact, testing didn't really have a clear idea of what they needed to prioritise as they always had so much work to review.

Daniel had learned this approach was far from ideal after reading "The Goal" by Eliyahu Goldratt, which highlights the importance of focussing on global throughput rather than local efficiencies.

In Goldratt's words, "Activating a non-bottleneck to its maximum is an act of maximum stupidity."

When a lion chases a dazzle of zebras, it will usually set its sight on its prey and focus to bring it home for its dinner. Previously, Daniel's team instead worked like a lion constantly switching targets and going home hungry at the end of the day.

Daniel had a proven gameplan to deal with this issue. The key was to minimise work-in-progress as much as possible. New work would not be added to the board until the old work was done.

From there, Daniel and Paul would review the stalest work and expedite it through to completion.

At first, the stale ticket reviews would take an hour every week but soon they became a slick process as the number of stale tickets declined.

Additionally, Daniel would set up alerts to detect when work was injected into the board outside the usual planning process.

If a ticket of work was set as in-progress but not on the board, it would automatically be pulled onto the board for visibility.

Daniel also created automated summaries of what the team had shipped in order to celebrate the work that was completed to keep people motivated.

Through all of this, and through educating the team that work would only deliver business value when it was shipped, Daniel was able to solve the problem.

Daniel said to Paul, "Before, the team would go through the motions of following an Agile methodology, but now we've actually made things agile. We don't do the weekly stand-up meetings anymore. We instead focussed on minimising work-in-progress as much as possible and that seems to work."

Paul interjected, "So we've become truly agile, but with what we're doing do we need to be truly agile?"

"Why don't we wait and see?" Daniel replied. "We don't need to change it if it's already optimised."

Daniel continued: "The team are happier as a result, and it seems burnout has gone down. Before, the work-in-progress was horrifically bad, but it isn't a limiting factor anymore – the requirements' engineering process is what we need to improve, so I don't see why we should make any changes either way on work-in-progress. The team are smart enough to manage things themselves when it comes down to this."

Paul nodded and they left the meeting room.

As Daniel walked past Mo's desk, Mo stopped him and said, "Dan, I've finished the spec and nominated a few to review it online – people in other teams we impact and such. I was wondering if you could take a look and do an in-person review with me when you get a second?"

"Sure, I've got time now. Why don't we grab a meeting room and look through it?" Daniel offered.

As Daniel and Mo sat in the meeting room looking up at the document on the large, screen Mo said, "I used a slightly different approach than we usually do when it comes to writing specs. So, the interesting thing was after I read the requirements document and listed any assumptions I'd made, the solution seemed to just pop out."

Mo continued: "Usually, we just outline the solution without any context; it's like the technology is there in want of a problem to solve."

"The challenge though comes because there are certain things which are unknown as to the direction they will ultimately take. For example," Mo went on, "we don't know if we'll ultimately need to sell this to more customers or if the customer could eventually want to access the data through a mobile app. What do you think I should do here?"

"So it seems there are two competing forces at play here. You don't want to complicate the architecture, but you want to have something that is resilient to change in the future?"

Mo replied, "Well, this is software – so it is meant to be soft."

"So instead of making the decision now, why don't you see to ensure they are reversible in future if possible?" Daniel said.

Mo summarised: "So we only implement what is necessary and we try and make it as simple as possible, but we don't box ourselves into a corner by making decisions that are needlessly hard to reverse later?"

"Exactly," Daniel replied. "Throughout my career, people have often gone on and on about the need for simplicity in software design, but then continue to produce the most complex software designs possible. Software that has to be deployed on complex infrastructure or is needlessly complex."

"I've been thinking about this a lot recently," Mo said. "Netflix has a very simple architecture when it comes to streaming movies around the world. They have a specific device they can send to Internet Service Providers or install in Internet Exchanges around the world. That device is able to ensure that content can be streamed quickly and cost-effectively to its customers. If they need to add more capacity, they add more of these servers."

Mo continued: "Altavista, the defunct search engine, required a specific hardware appliance. When Google came along, they could run their search engine software on any commodity hardware."

"You see the same pattern in modern Content Delivery Networks and cloud computing companies. Instead of having dedicated computing resources for all the different things they do, like security and performance, one server is able to provide all products the company needs. From there, the company just scales their infrastructure vertically the more resource they need," Mo concluded.

Daniel looked confused and said, "I'm not sure I understand. What's the underlying pattern you're trying to describe?"

"I guess the way I would describe it is that they have very simple architecture. There is one server that can do everything and they just scale that up as they need more capacity. Of course, that server needs to run lots of specific specialised software, but the point is that it can be packaged in such a way that it can do everything," Mo responded.

Daniel said, "These companies do also have specialised computing resources though for certain things, like databases and data analytics."

"Yes, of course they do," Mo replied, "but these aren't systems that need to scale in the same way, these offering services to the global network. You can buy Netflix in the US and use it in the UK without issue on the same app. You can access your Gmail regardless of where you are around the world using the same website."

"Very true," Daniel agreed, "and this is in contrast to many companies to have to run multiple different bespoke environments for different companies or customers in different geographies."

"So the way I would summarise it is: you try to avoid repeating yourself as much as possible. You try to maintain as few types of things that do fundamentally the same thing. One type of content distribution server which you can scale, one type of data processing pipeline you can grow when you need. Almost like successful budget airlines who stick to only one aircraft manufacturer, even if they're brand new, because the maintenance costs are so much more affordable," Mo stated.

Daniel said, "You know, this very much flies in the face of what is taught at software development conferences. There, engineers will often try to showcase their intellect through complex architectures. Cloud computing providers will sell dozens of products which fundamentally do the same thing in order to increase their revenue."

"I think business also plays a role in this, though," mused Mo. "Consider how many products we have which are fundamentally the same as those offered to other customers, just slightly modified but we have to run them in different environments for each customer. These should be homogenous systems you can scale infinitely, but instead they're snowflakes."

"Paul often tells me about the importance of product-market fit. You can test lots of ideas, but you need to find one which people love and be unafraid to pull the plug early when it doesn't prove viable," Daniel added.

"I agree," Mo concluded. "The problem seems to be businesses are too frightened to stop doing what doesn't work, so they nevertheless support broken products which only sell by becoming snowflakes."

Daniel's phone buzzed and looked at the notification on his phone screen. It was from Jess;

she had to make an academic trip to London the following week.

Executive Decisions

Daniel and Jess were walking along the south bank of the River Thames in London. It was dusk, but the lights on the bridges and those of the financial district on the other side of the river provided ample illumination.

"I'm not here for long," Jess said. "I just had to come examine a PhD defence. The university is back to doing them in-person and the candidate's research aligned with mine."

"Jess, I know you won't give me the technical answers, only the psychology, but I think there's something interesting I'm starting to realise with your work," Daniel said.

Jess nodded, encouraging Daniel to continue.

Daniel continued: "It seems loss aversion is also very much true in the business world. Companies will stick with products which are unprofitable because they're scared of losing the business, yet they require so much more money to maintain. This seems like a pretty clear case of loss aversion, right?"

Jess nodded again.

Daniel waited a moment for a police boat in the river to pass and then continued: "In the context of a company, why can't one person who isn't subject to loss aversion simply address the issue for the entire organisation?"

Jess said, "If we take the example of addiction, yes, there is treatment available, but what must someone do before they can benefit from the treatment?"

"Well, they need to actually want the treatment."

"Exactly," Jess replied, "so there's an executive decision someone needs to make. Just like someone can benefit from weight loss surgery, they must first themselves make the decision to undergo the treatment. Their knees might be in pain from the weight and the cells in their body crying out with inflammation, but ultimately there's a conscious decision that a small part of their brain needs to make."

Jess went on: "In a tech setting, for an executive who simply wants a painkiller, they can just engineer out the noisy employee who's doing work to bring about change. Research has shown that 75% of software engineers who report wrongdoing faced retaliation the last time they spoke up to raise the alarm to issues."

"So someone fairly low down the chain in junior or middle management is incapable of making change?" Daniel reflected.

Jess replied, "Not necessarily, but almost always. However, you can improve your own work centre that you control if you're given the freedom to do so, as is the situation in your case. If you're not given this freedom though, you can face retaliation for doing things your manager doesn't like."

"Jess, you're being incredibly depressing here if you don't mind me saying…"

"What makes you think this is depressing?" Jess interjected.

"Well, you're saying that people rarely change and there's no way for a junior person in a hierarchy to bring that change about," Daniel replied.

"For starters", Jess responded, "I don't actually think this is that depressing of a conversation; there's actually quite an optimistic message here. But to start with, what right do you think someone has to bring about change when the people in the hierarchy are opposed to it? Do you truly know what is better for someone else than they themselves do?"

Daniel replied, "Well, don't we always strive for excellence? Don't we always want to be better?"

"Your upbringing wasn't the easiest, was it?" Jess questioned. "Your parents would fight constantly, abuse each other and take their anger out on you. How did you get out of that situation?"

As they passed a bench by the river, they sat down. Fortunately, the weather was mild and dry, and they were both suitably dressed for the temperature.

Daniel thought for a moment and then started to talk "Well…in the end I left home when I was 18. I found work and funded my own way through university. I don't really talk with my parents anymore."

"This might sound harsh, but don't you think you could have changed your parents?" Jess asked.

"Maybe that's what drives my own internal longing for continuous improvement here," Daniel posited. "The fact I failed at a young age to save my parents from their own inability to resolve their problems."

"That's probably the trauma that drives me too," Jess shared. "I couldn't save my mother from herself and perhaps that guilt drives me to this day."

Jess looked at Daniel in these eyes and said to him, "However, it's really important you understand you cannot force people to change. They have their own agency and autonomy. Also, it can often be important for people to learn from their own mistakes."

Jess continued: "Lawyers will often consider companies as people, but they have their own executive functions which you can't change."

"If change is so hard, how come it's the very force of natural selection that enables us to exist on this earth? Surely we would have had to be at least somewhat tolerant of change in order to survive?" asked Daniel.

London is home to many urban foxes which roam the streets at night, and Jess gained sight of one attacking a half-eaten burger someone had abandoned. Whilst the fox was certainly no wolf, it gave Jess an idea.

"Daniel, where does the phrase lone wolf come from?"

"Well, isn't it when a wolf leaves their pack to go it themselves?"

"Precisely," Jess answered. "Wolves don't overthrow the social structure of their pack – they go it alone. Setting aside the cases where there are ethical problems, this is also what happens in the workplace. People who aren't happy tend to quietly leave and do their own thing."

Jess went on: "About two years ago, I was flying from Singapore to the Netherlands. I was sat next to a young Dutch software engineer called Laura. She worked for a failing bank. She was a good engineer – rather than focussing on technology she focussed on outcomes. The bank was dependant on taxpayer funds but expected to stand on its own two feet, something it was struggling to do. She told me how she would try to 'manage up', but she was ignored. Loss aversion was strong. The reason she was on that flight is she was taking her remaining holiday leave since she was leaving her job."

Jess looked down and said, "I have encountered so many of these same situations, time and time again people try and implement change but fail so they leave. It is the universal truth of what happens when trying to manage up in a disaster zone."

Daniel said: "Okay, but you've not answered my point about how humans survive."

"So how does change happen in evolution?" Jess asked.

Daniel instinctively recited, "Survival of the fittest."

"So think about what that actually means. The implication is the weakest die," Jess stated.

Daniel said, "So in the business world, the fitness function is the ability to make money or keep raising investment – when that fails, death occurs."

"Precisely."

Daniel laughed and said, "So what you're saying is that we should kill ourselves, so our parents don't have any offspring?"

Jess laughed, sharing in Daniel's dark sense of humour. "Well, we need to put evolution in context. Lasting evolutionary change takes millions of years. Epigenetics seems to indicate that how these genes are expressed can matter on what your mother endured. If your mother is underweight or overweight during pregnancy, that can very much be a predictor of obesity. Speaking of which, I'm starving," Jess said abruptly. "Do you want to get chips?"

As they began to walk away from the river towards a nearby takeaway, Jess went on. "Evolution is slow, but we see it happen in the corporate world too. Companies unable to survive will go bankrupt and others will replace them."

"Okay," Daniel said, "let's take another process of improvement. Theory of Constraints teaches us a focussing process to look at what matters most and then improve that continuously until it's no longer a problem."

"In other words 'take apart whatever is holding me back,'" Jess reflected.

Daniel nodded and said, "Yeah, pretty much. That is an artificial process, but is it fundamentally just accelerating evolution?"

They walked inside the takeaway and ordered chips. As Jess paid by waving her watch over the card reader, the young man behind the counter poured salt and vinegar over the chips.

As they walked back to the river, Jess continued the conversation. "I think both paradigms are similar. I recently consulted for a start-up which achieved some remarkable things. I personally saw more personal growth working there than I ever had during my career."

Jess continued: "The team at the company were truly remarkable and you could see the growth in all of them. They literally hired one of their engineers from a warzone in Syria and got him to Egypt where he now works remotely."

Jess prodded a chip with a small wooden fork and said, "They achieved all that on the paradigm of focussing on the biggest business risk they faced and addressing it. In their personal lives, they would essentially adopt the same process."

"So what seems to be the predictors for someone being capable of embarking on such a process of personal change?" Daniel asked.

Jess said, "This is the enigma. Just earlier today I was reading a study of how patient's sex, medical insurance, psychiatric history, co-morbidities, and even counselling doesn't seem to predict whether people will be successful in weight loss programs."

Jess concluded, "This is what the project you're working on now will help us to understand."

Implementation

It was morning when Paul hurriedly arrived at Daniel's desk. With him were a couple of well-dressed colleagues.

"Hi Dan," Paul began, "this is James and Ian from the sales team. They have someone else in need of the clinical trials system that Mo is currently building. What I was thinking is that we could maybe spin up a different version of the software for them, with their customisations on."

"I really want us to help these customers out," Daniel said, "but we have a lot of bespoke software here already, and we can't maintain another snowflake."

One of the two men said, "Hi Dan, I'm James. The customer is really keen to get this software, so anything we can do to pull it out of the hat would be amazing. One of the other engineering teams was able to duplicate their bespoke software for this team, and while it has been a headache, it really helped us out."

"Is that the cash accounting software?" Daniel asked.

James nodded.

Daniel had heard horror stories about this project. The cash accounting system was duplicated for another client and required customisations, meaning the team were struggling to make updates for multiple clients. Moreover, even where there was functionality that was shared between the systems, one customer would want to control their release funnel at a different schedule to the other.

The matter wasn't helped by the fact that in this highly regulated environment, the bespoke customisations had caused multiple incidents. Being on the on-call rota, Daniel was well familiar with being woken up in the early hours of the morning after something would break.

The engineering manager for the team ultimately resigned after coming under intense pressure for the quality of work completed and having the regulatory blame placed on his shoulders.

At this point, Daniel had to balance not upsetting the salesmen – who would run to the Chief Technology Officer and demand the work be undertaken regardless – with also ensuring he wouldn't suffer the same fate as the engineering manager for the cash accounting team.

Daniel carefully asked, "What is it they're looking for?"

The other man, presumably Ian, replied, "Well, they essentially want the same clinical trials system. They want the user interface to match their internal system, but they also wanted it to integrate with their login system."

"I couldn't think of any other way we could implement this, given it diverges from what Red Phoenix want for their system, so let's just duplicate the system," James added.

Nodding, Ian interjected, "That's exactly why we did the same with the cash accounting system."

Daniel looked flabbergasted. "Is there any other reason they want a different system? Any data isolation requirements? Any major customisations?"

The salesmen shook their heads.

Daniel was speechless. Complex data isolation or large code changes could still be managed whilst avoiding the need to create another snowflake, but the underlying reasons they were proposing to do this were certainly no grounds to do so.

Programmers will often joke that all problems in computer science can be solved by another level of indirection. In this case, it was never truer.

Implementing a theming system which would allow the design of the application to be customised and then implementing the ability to swap out the built-in login system with single sign-on would be relatively straightforward.

As Daniel explained this, the salespeople seemed happy with the proposal.

Daniel then asked, "Out of curiosity, why didn't you explain the problem in the first place? Why did you come with a solution proposed?"

James looked uneasy and said, "Well, first of all, we didn't know if you'd have wanted to come to the customer meeting, so we had to propose a solution for them there and then. I think they'll be happier with what you've said now, we just need to manage the message."

"The other thing is that when we worked with the cash accounting team, they weren't really interested in what the customer wanted," Ian added. "They had their vision for the technology and wanted to implement that, so we had to find a way around that."

"Their focus was the technology, not the actual value it would provide to the customers," James said, nodding.

As they walked away, Daniel turned to Paul and said, "Could you make sure before they sign that contract that we look over what work we've committed to doing for them? If possible, would be great if we could get some requirements to work with, if not have a meeting with them first."

"Sure," Paul replied. "I want to get as many customers calls in as possible; it really helps me do market research if this is a product we end up scaling to other customers."

Daniel called Mo over and explained what was happening.

"No worries," Mo replied, "we're almost done well ahead of schedule on the project, so I'll be ready to start when the contract is signed. We could actually demo it today. The hold-up is with the QA team. They're understaffed, and they have no one to help us with this."

Daniel looked over to his desk at his laptop screen with the Kanban board open. "Is there anything else on your plate right now, Mo?"

"Not really, just technical debt, cleaning up old code and some really old bugs."

Thinking out loud, Daniel wondered, "Why do we need a QA engineer on this at all? You've done the specification, the frontend, and the backend. You even did the scientific work as you became the subject matter expert in the problem space. Why can't you do the quality assurance yourself too?"

"It's been great to own a project from start to finish," Mo shared. "I'd love to do the testing, that way I can make sure the tests are automatically run instead of in a manually run test plan. But will QA mind? Won't they want some independent oversight of the process?"

"I mean, there's no regulatory need to have the system audited but they'll get sight of it before it goes live to real users. That said, both Jess and Red Phoenix will do acceptance testing before it goes live. The data integrity system also manages risk through a complete audit trail," Daniel explained.

Daniel thought further and said, "But what we can offer to satisfy them in case there's any issues is we can let them run the automated tests and see exactly what the robot is doing and what behaviour is coming out. That will help give them the assurance that it's right and empower them to do the testing whenever they want. Let me go speak to the QA team and hear what they have to say."

A few minutes later, Daniel walked past Julian's desk; he had always felt that messages on the internal instant messaging system were too impersonal. Julian was the engineering manager for the QA team and clearly looked exhausted. He proceeded to explain the situation, apprehensive as to the response.

Julian's eyes lit up. "I love it. The reason we're in this mess is that so much work is thrown over the fence to QA these past few days without any testing first. The engincering teams just care about the code, not the impact on users. Instead of worrying about the problem they're solving, the engineers act as if they're just there to produce computer code. If this works, maybe we can get other teams on board too."

Daniel smiled and thanked Julian. He went back to tell Mo.

"Mo, Paul," Daniel said, "book your flights to Australia next week. Let's demo this."

Change Potential

That evening was date night for Daniel. He was cooking dinner with Emily, his partner of 10 years.

"I'm sorry things have been so busy at work recently", Daniel said.

"It's been crazy for me too," Emily replied. "What have you been working on recently?"

"Before I explain, I have a question for you."

Emily turned towards Daniel, and he continued: "So we both had pretty dysfunctional parents growing up. They never seemed able to solve the problems they faced. Why don't we face the same issue? Do we solve problems better?"

Emily said, "Well, we all have different ways of solving problems – doesn't mean one way is wrong and another way isn't."

Emily went on: "We don't really argue ever, but the first time we had a misunderstanding years ago, we both just talked about the issue and addressed it. We both wanted to solve the problem, so we did. Both our parents would argue about things like money a lot, but we put our relationship first."

Daniel paused from the potato he was peeling and said to Emily, "You really had to fight yourself out of hell when you became an adult. You grew up in awful circumstances but nevertheless succeeded. How did you manage it?"

"Well, I was motivated to", said Emily. "You know, I was reading that some evolutionary scientists wrote a paper where they argued that depression evolved to help us deal with complex problems."

"That's interesting. So how does that work?"

Emily said, "Well, the theory goes that depression helps people ruminate, so our ancestors would be able to stay focussed on complex interpersonal problems until they're resolved."

Daniel replied, "Jess, who I'm working on this project with, tells me there's a lot in the human brain which stops us being able to address issues – so it makes sense that there's something to counterbalance that and actually address problems."

"Yes," Emily replied, "but in society right now our focus seems to be not on solving the problems but taking the pain away through antidepressants. Don't get me wrong, I'm certain antidepressants play an important role in many instances but seems like the encouragement to solve problems also needs to be there. I guess that's basically what therapy is – working through your problems."

Daniel said, "So you think motivation was a key part in solving your problems?"

"Well, not just motivation, self-motivation specifically. It had to come from within. When someone tries to force you to do something, you resist them," Emily replied.

She looked at Daniel and said, "You never forced me to address issues, but you helped me believe that I could address the problems; before I used to think they were insurmountable."

Daniel looked Emily in the eyes and said, "Me too – you've helped me overcome a lot because you told me to have the belief in myself to address the issues."

Emily said, "You know, this is something I've heard a lot from people who've done work in education. These elite schools that some children go to – yes, the networking and education helps, but apparently a huge part is them just being told they can do anything they want and giving them the confidence to do so."

Emily then said, "Well, of course if your self-belief vastly exceeds your abilities or you're a narcissist, you might not listen to feedback early enough to solve problems and keep following the same path when things are going wrong. So, I guess there's a balancing act of sorts here."

Daniel turned on the air fryer so it would start preheating and began cutting the peeled potatoes into chips.

Daniel said, "Do you think there's almost something which is intrinsic about people's ability to change? Things like intelligence are based on both people's environmental and genetic factors?"

Emily said, "I mean, depression is somewhat hereditary but that doesn't mean mental health issues can't affect everyone."

Daniel opened a pack of steak burgers and put them in the air fryer with the potatoes. As the fan in the air fryer continued to whir, they stood in thought for a few seconds.

Emily eventually returned herself to the present and said, "You know, with children we have to teach them how to regulate their emotions. The instinct is to give up and throw a tantrum, but they learn the need to persist through the challenges."

"That isn't to say persisting is always the best idea though," Emily said. "In an abusive relationship or toxic work environment, the best idea might just be to leave."

"So how do you teach children self-regulation skills?" Daniel asked.

Emily replied, "Well, emotional attunement is a big part of it. You first have to pay attention to their emotions and validate them, then you can coach them to solve their problems. If you fail at this, they might not be able to do self-attunement later in life."

Emily continued: "Inconsistency when it comes to emotional needs gives rise to an anxious attachment style, where someone can validate their emotions but not address problems. Those with anxious attachment style can struggle with stress and change. Avoidant attachment style, which is where I think we both are, means we are more likely to suppress emotions but focus on solving problems."

Daniel asked: "What about those with secure attachment styles? Are there others?"

"Yeah, there's disorganised attachment style too which is inconsistent and hard to predict. About half of people have secure attachment style, though."

Daniel took some cheddar cheese slices out of the fridge, and back at the counter he began to slice open two buns and put them in the toaster.

"So," Daniel summarised, "in order to make these substantial life changes, you need to be self-motivated, have self-belief in your abilities but still be receptive to feedback, and also good at self-regulating your emotions."

"Yes," Emily agreed, "and I think these traits are musclebuilding. Sure, some people might have more natural talent than others, but you can always train and self-improve."

Daniel said, "You know, this aligns with what I've been hearing at work. There was a study which found that leaders who prioritise workforce emotions are about almost 3 times more likely to be successful in digital transformations."

Analysis

Daniel was in Australia again. This time, he was joined by his colleagues Paul and Mo.

Instead of going to Sydney, they were meeting at Red Phoenix's offices in Melbourne. Today was the day they were to meet the client and see if they were happy with their solution.

Both Jess and Red Phoenix's QA team had access to the Project Renegade web interface and had been testing it. The team sat in the board room and there was only a matter of minutes until the others would join.

The whole team were drinking their coffee nervously as they awaited judgement. Daniel had missed the coffee in Australia. People used to tell him the coffee in Melbourne was amazing, but he never appreciated it until he tried it himself.

Mo was usually a backend software engineer, but he had pretty much handled the entire project from the specification, through to the implementation of the backend systems and user interface alongside doing the testing himself.

Mo was painfully aware that if a requirement was missed in the specification, it would cascade the entire way down to testing.

Mo suddenly panicked. "Dan, do you have an adapter for my laptop? I forgot my HDMI dongle, so I don't know how to present my screen in the meeting."

As Daniel began to scramble in his bag, Paul calmly put his hand on Daniel's shoulder and said, "Relax. There's a HDMI socket on the side of your new laptop."

Mo laughed and savoured the moment of relief as he plugged the cable directly into his laptop.

Paul said confidently, "The design looks sharp, Mo."

"Thank you," Mo replied. "I did the frontend work myself, though I have to admit the design team did help with the icons."

Before long, the others joined them. Jess and the Red Phoenix team, led by Vu, walked in.

In Daniel's experience, Vu had always been exceptionally kind. The sales team would describe him as harsh, but Daniel suspected this was because they would try to sell him solutions without the engineering understanding to know what he was looking for.

However, Daniel couldn't help but think back on the meeting Sydney and what had happened to the previous team who worked on this project.

"Thanks for coming down," Vu said. "I appreciate it's been a long trip. The reason we wanted you here in person is so you can understand how the software is actually being used."

Vu continued: "I'll be straight with you. We didn't want this project delivered early but of substandard quality or massively overbudget. I've had enough of that happening with our outsourcing partners. This is the first time in a while that software has been delivered on-time, on-budget and up to the quality requirements we have."

"We were so impressed," Vu went on, "we've already given access to one of the research teams to begin testing. They've got some suggestions for changes they want to see."

Paul responded, "Thanks, I'm glad this meets your expectations. In all honesty, we threw away the rulebook and we just focussed on delivering an impact, not on our usual Agile development methodology. What kind of changes did you have in mind?"

"Well, the team compiled a list," Vu replied. "None are blockers to launch, but there's a few we'd like to see in place as soon as possible. I'll email them over now."

Mo pulled up the document on his screen.

Paul turned to Daniel and said, "Dan, some of these seem quite straightforward. What kind of approach are we going to use to ship these? Do we need specifications?"

"So to fill the Red Phoenix team in on the approach we've used here," Daniel explained, "we started by analysing your requirements, getting them documented, and then turning this into a technical specification. We reviewed this internally and Paul liaised with some folks on your team to keep you in the loop on the solution we were looking at. We then implemented this solution using a Lean software development lifecycle."

Recognising Vu's confused look, Daniel clarified what Lean software development is. "We focussed more on completing work than starting it. Essentially, we minimised the amount of concurrent work, let Mo own the work from start to finish, and addressed problems when they came up."

Vu interjected, saying, "Ah, we still call that just-in-time manufacturing. So, you used rigorous requirements engineering, then Lean practices for the actual development. So now what you're thinking about is how rigorously you'll stick to the new process?"

"Right," Daniel said. "What do you think Mo?"

Mo thought about the question and then slowly said, "For large work, I think the requirements, documents, and specifications were important, but for some of these tasks I can just use a support ticket or a ticket on our board to track them. For example, changing a bit of copy in the user interface. Some other bits, like this data export functionality, should probably have a specification document."

Paul added, "There's also some things here which the requirements are a bit unclear for. For example, you want to use keyboard shortcuts, but we don't know what shortcuts to use. Or the additional statistical analysis features. We don't know yet what statistical measures you want."

"In all honesty, I don't think we know either," Vu stated. "We were looking to you to help guide that. Our team are here if you want to do market research."

Paul nodded and replied, "Yes, that makes sense. With Mo, I can ask some market research questions – one of us will ask the questions and the other will ensure the process isn't biased. We could also watch them use the product itself and maybe experiment."

"I agree," Mo said. "That's the one thing I think we've been missing in this process. Clearly there's some frustration with the user interface here, but I've not seen anyone use the product yet, so I've not felt this pain yet."

"Don't be harsh with yourself," Vu said. "You need something you can start with before you can experiment."

Paul leaned back and started saying, "So we have this list of things we probably want to get through, but which will we get to first?"

Daniel noticed Jess smiling as Vu said, "Well, the choice is yours. Nothing is particularly urgent right now."

"Perhaps the first thing we should do is prioritise what is most important, by measurement or talking to people and then go from there," Daniel ventured.

Paul nodded and said, "That works for me. If we have a yardstick of what the biggest problems are, we can work to solve them first."

"Paul and Mo, come with us and we'll introduce you to the team so you can do your research," Vu concluded. He looked to Daniel and said, "Jess will also be around today if you have any questions on the scientific side."

Experimentation

Daniel and Jess were last to leave the meeting room and began to walk outside the building. Jess put on her sunglasses while Daniel fumbled to replace his prescription glasses with his prescription sunglasses.

"Congrats," Jess said.

Daniel started saying, "The delivery wasn't actually that hard. We just did…"

"Proper engineering practice?" Jess interjected, smiling.

"I wonder how we'll manage to trace the requirements back the further we diverge from the specification though," Daniel pondered.

"This has worked well so far, I'm not going to start giving you the answers to your engineering problems, certainly not overtly. Remember, it's not my job to make you undergo any changes at all," Jess said.

Jess was amused, and although Daniel also seemed amused, he also seemed slightly exasperated that Jess continued to refuse to talk about engineering matters.

"You know," Daniel said, "when we get back, we're going to start working on a project to turn this platform into a service another company can also use with some modifications."

They approached a crossing, though Daniel was unsure where Jess was going. He hoped she wasn't also following him.

"What's the problem?" Jess asked. "The agreement with Red Phoenix lets you make changes and only charges them a monthly fee for using the service, so it's completely what they expect. And it seems like the architecture of the system should allow it with ease – you haven't done anything which would engineer you into a corner preventing you from making the system multitenant, right?"

Daniel replied, "We are now building a Software-as-a-Service project instead of a standalone product. We're building for multiple customers, not just one. The engineering isn't what I'm thinking about, it's how we interact with the customers."

"I was thinking about what Paul was saying in that meeting about wanting experimentation, but becoming a Software-as-a-Service product changes how we experiment to find what our users want," Daniel said.

"So it's not a problem," Jess countered, "it's an opportunity to test new ideas as to what you build?"

"Yeah," Daniel replied. "Remember when you talked about the pain-pleasure balance? Well, big social media firms will test to find out what keeps users addicted. That's how they hack their dopamine systems."

As a tram passed them, they arrived at a classically architected building. They walked up a set of stairs and sat on a park bench.

"Where are we?" Daniel asked.

"State Library Victoria," Jess replied. "Busiest library in Australia and the third busiest library in the world. Speaking of dopamine, I'm a member so I get a discount on the coffee too."

Daniel continued from earlier: "Right, so I've heard about these companies who will use A/B testing to test things which work on a large userbase. Can't we do something like get answers on what features we make?"

"You can," Jess said "Let's circle back to our conversation on change. What role do you think experimentation has in change?"

"Experimentation seems fundamental," Daniel said. "How else do you know what works or not? How do you know something isn't doing more harm than good?"

"True," Jess replied, "people who weigh themselves daily are more likely to be successful at losing weight than those who do so weekly. So how do these big tech giants use A/B testing?"

Daniel said, "Well, they'll have a proportion of their userbase who are randomly put into having a new experience. Another set who will have the old experience, and you see what changes. You run some statistics and you see what works best."

"You know, in medicine and psychology they use this a lot – we call them randomised control trials. That's how we really find out which drugs and vaccines work. It's a pretty robust form of scientific evaluation," Jess said.

She continued: "However, there's a few things you're missing. Firstly, not all humans are the same."

Daniel looked confused and said, "I know when it comes to change, there are many forces which aren't rational – but we are all human. I mean, 99.9% of our genetic make-up is the same."

Jess explained, "During the COVID-19 pandemic, professors Peter Horby and Martin Landray successfully found the first life-saving treatment to COVID-19. They ran a large-scale clinical trial across almost 200 National Health Service hospitals in the UK. In just 9 months after the discovery, the finding was estimated to save a million lives around the world through a common low-cost drug."

Jess went on, saying, "The twist was that this drug, dexamethasone, was found to lead to lead to the best improvement amongst those in ventilated patients, reducing the death rate by a third. Patients on ventilation are those at the highest risk of death. For those on oxygen only, the death rate was reduced only by 20%. The drug didn't make a difference for those who had no help breathing."

Jess concluded, "What I'm getting at is that we must look into sub-groups, and just because something helps one person, or even a majority, doesn't mean it will help everyone. A treatment could show no effect even though it radically helps some people but harms others."

"So that's why even when the rates of personal change are low, whether it comes to overcoming addiction or a corporate transformation, you don't write off everyone's experiences off?"

"Precisely," Jess replied. "I've seen many environments where tech workers, who don't understand science more generally, have become trapped by the assumption that everyone is the same. In electronic systems, there is often only one root cause for an issue, but when it comes to humans, there can be many causes that contribute to a problem, particularly at a population-wide level."

Jess continued: "By treating everyone the same, we remove their agency and individuality. In one organisation I studied, I saw how an engineering manager who was a self-taught scientist sought to blame someone on his team who was part of a minority group for the fact that he was being treated differently."

Jess was clearly becoming more passionate as she spoke. "In the book, Knowing You, the neuroscientist Anil Seth explores just how differently we each see the world. One example is how Russian speakers see more shades of blue as there's more vocabulary for it in Russian. A few years ago, you may remember seeing a photo going around the internet as to whether a dress was blue and black, or white and gold."

"It was definitely blue and black," Daniel said with a smile.

"That was true for me too," Jess said, "but not for everyone, and it seems to be based in whether their brains assumed it was lit by artificial light or natural light based on their past experiences. This is why we cannot assume that everyone is the same when we do experimentation like this."

Jess continued: "The start-up incubator YCombinator will often say that it's better to find just 10 customers who absolutely love your start-up over a 1000 who just like it. This ties in with the danger of scaling too fast before you find product-market fit with just a few users initially."

Daniel could see Jess's passion. "Okay," he responded, "that all makes sense, but if we account for sub-groups, why can't we just run all the experiments we want to find what people need?"

Jess replied, "So the randomised control trial is supposedly the gold standard experimentation technique. Why do you think that the tech aging companies which do nothing but A/B testing on their web platforms haven't taken over the world? Why can start-ups disrupt them?"

"Well, there are many causes – but I'm not really sure," Daniel said.

Jess replied, "This kind of testing is what happens when you don't have a strong hypothesis and vision and are just testing to see what happens. When we do clinical trials, it's best practice to preregister your study so people know what you're looking for. This helps stops the effect of scientists dredging data and creating a hypothesis after the fact."

Daniel thought carefully and said, "I see. So, running a scientific experiment without a hypothesis is like engineering without collecting requirements first. You need to have a hypothesis by understanding the mechanics before you do an experiment, but you can always update the hypothesis later as you get more information."

"Pretty much. And one last thing on this before we get coffee," Jess said. "In science, when we run these experiments, we often reach for absurd levels of confidence that our answer is right. This is important when testing drugs and vaccines, but for the colour of a button, it's often acceptable just be confident on the balance of probabilities."

Standing up, Jess said, "Sometimes it can take so long to get the data, it's best to go for gut feel and then change the decision later where needed, especially when you're making low-risk, reversible, engineering judgements."

Daniel stood up too and said, "Okay, but then how do we know what works and what doesn't work?"

"Well, there are a few ways," Jess explained. "You can use Lean Startup techniques to test a business idea by only building a Minimum Viable Product and you can use the concepts in the book The Mom Test to do market validation interviews in a way which doesn't bias the test subject."

Jess concluded, "All this is designed to stop you wasting your time on things you just don't need in order to find out how to make an impact."

Daniel nodded and said, "Not everything needs to be scientific. Sometimes the most important thing is making an impact."

"Yes," Jess replied, "scientific rigour has it's time and place. Now we're at the time and place for coffee."

Delay Gratification

Jess was clearly happy to finally have her coffee in front of her, and Daniel was resisting the urge to point out how she should perhaps reduce her caffeine intake to better care for her own dopamine receptors.

However, Daniel had a more pressing question on his mind.

"Jess," Daniel said, "I know we shouldn't try to change people, but if someone wants to go down the route of change, what can we do to help them achieve that?"

"Have you heard of the Stanford marshmallow experiment?" asked Jess.

Daniel shook his head, so Jess began to explain. "In 1970, an experiment was conducted to test whether a child would rather take an immediate reward of a single marshmallow or wait for a bit and take two. This experiment tested their ability to delay for a larger reward later, delay gratification. Those who could had better life outcomes later."

"So what controls how good we are at delay gratification?" Daniel inquired.

Jess took a sip of her coffee and said, "There are a few predictors; the need for achievement, being a perfectionist, and the ability to experience positive emotions are examples. Conscientiousness is perhaps the most significant predictor – the personality trait of being responsible, careful, or diligent,"

"I mean, those are interesting," Daniel replied, "but these are fairly deeply embedded traits – is there anything we can readily do to control delay gratification ability?"

"So there are two key approaches," Jess explained. "One is where people try to use sheer willpower to get themselves to delay the gratification. The problem is that the research indicates this ability goes quickly – people get burnt out. A quarter of New Year's resolutions are broken by the second week of January."

Jess continued: "The second approach relies in using emotions to delay gratification. The psychologist David DeSteno found that, on average, people would accept $17 now instead of $100."

Daniel interjected, "Wow, I'd sure love a bank that would give me about six times the money if I just waited a year."

Jess nodded. "Definitely, and the interesting thing is that being happy didn't seem to make a difference to this. However, if people were first primed to feel gratitude, it would instead take $30 for them to turn down the offer of a $100 in a year. So, gratitude nearly doubled the ability to delay gratification."

"That's remarkable," Daniel said. "Are there any other emotions that have this effect?"

Jess nodded. "So, David DeSteno wrote a book on this called Emotional Success. In there, he argues that the emotions of gratitude, compassion, and pride enhance the ability to delay gratification. These emotions encourage us to place more value on the future."

Jess said, "In the past, a technique I've used with engineering teams during transformation exercises is to get them to do retrospectives where they look back over the last couple of weeks, but instead, get them to categorise what has made them grateful, compassionate, and proud. This is of course after the science, and what we're trying to achieve has been explained to them, so they're willing participants. From my experience, it definitely leaves the team with a very powerful emotional effect."

"I wonder if this has an effect in people's personal lives?" Daniel asked.

Jess replied quickly. "Oh, definitely. Delay gratification has been linked to happy, long-lasting marriages. Also, the children who participated in the Stanford marshmallow experiment were followed-up with decades later and those with better delay gratification abilities had better life outcome measures and educational attainment."

Daniel sat in silence for a moment. You've given me a lot to think about. But it's getting late, I think I should get back to my hotel", he said.

Rewind and Repeat

Daniel, Mo, and Paul were transiting through Singapore's Changi airport. With a few hours until their flight, they decided to take advantage of the airside pool the airport had on offer.

As they sat on the poolside, Daniel asked Mo, "So how did you find the time in Australia?"

"Very useful," Mo replied. "We finally got to see the product in use and see what they actually wanted with those suggestions."

"The one thing I worry about is how we're going to keep track of requirements with this mix of large and small tasks," Daniel said. "Clearly the small tasks don't need specification documents, but how do we track the requirements?"

Mo said, "I think I already have that sorted. Traceability of requirements is important, but because we already log our work against tickets, there's a ticket for each requirement. The ticket can then link back to a specification document, a support ticket, or just quote a conversation or some market research that Paul has done. It's fairly straightforward, actually."

Mo went on: "There's also something else though too. Since I've been able to write the software tests as I work through this, essentially using Test Driven-Development instead of waiting for QA, there are tests in the codebase which link back to requirements. That means the requirements are essentially living in the code itself."

Mo asked Daniel, "Why did you want to make sure that it was there?"

Daniel replied, "I just wanted to make sure we had an understanding of the context of why certain features are implemented, I didn't want this to be a situation years later where we have snowflakes we can't maintain."

Paul was out of the pool and within ear shot of the conversation. "Moaning about snowflakes again?", he said smiling. "We've actually got quite a good solution to that."

Daniel looked intrigued.

Mo explained: "Well, a few weeks ago, we remember you saying how we should be less loss averse when it comes to killing off features we don't need, so what we did is we now have analytics within the product. If we test something and it doesn't work, we can add a warning to show that it's going, turn it off, and then remove it."

"Won't sales or marketing be less than happy with that?" Daniel asked.

"Come on, would you buy a new TV remote just because it had double the buttons?" Paul asked. "People want things of value."

Mo added, "We asked sales and marketing, and they are happy with this. They want to focus on what sells. We also told them how less complexity means we can ship what customers want faster and that seemed to seal the deal."

"Good work," Daniel said. "You know, I think more so than having a documented requirements engineering process, the most important thing has actually been making sure what we're building is actually necessary. Like, does it solve the problem that the customers want us to solve?"

"And making sure the implementation remains true to that," Mo chimed in. "No more words lost in translation."

Daniel then said, "Mo, you're typically a backend software developer. How did you feel about owning this project from start to finish?"

Mo had managed to get his hands on a colourful looking soft drink but nevertheless replied, "It's been really satisfying to see the real-world impact of my work from start to finish. I'd be lying if I said I hadn't learnt a lot. I had to learn a lot of information about the problem space and the challenges I needed to solve. Paul and the engineers with speciality in the technology I needed were able to help, no doubt."

Mo went on: "Of course, there were things I couldn't do myself, like design, but help wasn't too far away. When these things came up, I just treated them as if I was buying a part for something I'm building. Like if you're building a car, it's fine that you don't know how to make a tire if you can buy one off the shelf. Airplane manufacturers don't need to buy engines when they can get them from Rolls-Royce."

Paul stood up, presumably to get a drink himself, and said, "You know, I have a bit of an interest in structural engineering myself. Arup is the engineering firm that has engineered the Sydney Opera House, The Shard alongside the London Eye, Singapore Flyer, and Vegas High Roller. Their engineering philosophy very much rested on the idea that the engineer works early in a project with the architect. I can see the rationale for that given how we're working now."

Identifying Necessity

Two weeks later, the software went live without issue, with all the changes Red Phoenix wanted. From Australia, Vu had ordered a box of doughnuts for the team as a thank you, sent by a local bakery in London.

The team were ecstatic, and the management team of N. X. T. Systems praised Daniel on successfully leading the project.

Daniel had booked out a meeting room for the go-live, but with everything online without issue, he turned to Mo and Paul. "We've turned our backs on much of the Agile project management philosophy, but what process have we replaced this with here?"

Paul said, "So the first thing we do in an engineering project now is we define the problem. We don't start with the solution or a partial solution, we start with the actual pain-point the customer is facing. We focus on defining that well."

"Definitely," Daniel commented, "and that way we reduce the risk of changes later in the process, building something the customer doesn't need, or their being communication issues later."

Mo started to speak. "The next step is then we find the solution. If the problem is defined well enough and the assumptions are listed, the solution often just falls out with limited engineering."

"And we use the best tool for the job to capture the requirements and the system design, sometimes that means a specification document but other times just a ticket will suffice."

Mo continued: "We then implement the solution, and we essentially avoid task switching by keeping work-in-progress down."

"That means we don't follow Agile for the sake of it," Paul remarked. "If problems come up, we address them by addressing the biggest risks."

"Then we repeat as we need to," Daniel concluded.

Paul said, "It's surprising that 70% of software projects failed to be delivered on-time, when such simple solutions are readily available if we just use common sense."

"Thanks everyone," Mo said, wrapping up. "It's getting late, so I think we best finish off the doughnuts and then head home."

Growth

Daniel arrived home and Emily was waiting for him.

"Things went well," Daniel said.

"That's good", Emily replied.

"You're always so busy and you've had to travel so much recently, so I'm glad it's done", Emily continued.

Daniel said, "I hope Jess's research is successful in helping people achieve personal changes in their lives. I know what I've learned has already been beneficial."

"So, in the end, what was it you learned about achieving change in people?" Emily asked.

"Well," Daniel replied, "firstly, I think it's important to recognise it isn't your job to force a company or an individual to change. Many books on management and transformation claim that it is, but it ultimately would end in misery. Instead, you can give people the tools and knowledge to do so."

Daniel added, "Secondly, where someone is keen to make changes, you can enhance their ability to delay gratification for a greater reward later by reminding them of reasons to be grateful, proud, and compassionate."

"Finally," Daniel concluded, "to be good at change, we need to be self-motivated, believe in ourselves, and be good at self-regulating our emotions. Being conscientiousness is something else which helps us on this journey. We should practice these skills like a muscle."

Emily looked impressed but Daniel went on: "There was something pretty important you taught me too. We both have avoidant attachment styles which means we're self-reliant and focus on resolving issues. However, other people have greater emotional needs than we do before they can resolve problems."

Emily handed Daniel a bottle of sparkling wine. Taking a tablecloth, he opened it and poured two glasses.

Taking a sip, Emily said, "I think we've both made such significant personal changes in our lives. We should both be proud of what we've achieved."

Daniel replied, "Definitely. There's something else, though. The approach to continuous improvement that Jess taught me was simple. Take apart whatever is holding you back, identify your biggest risk, and mitigate it. If you are too scared to lose your demons, your problems will mount."

Daniel took a pause and said, "The biggest risk I face right now is not spending enough time with you. I've spent enough time at work, making money for the taxman, I think it's time we spend some time to ourselves."

Emily smiled. "Okay, well what do you want to do?"

"Well, I got a lot of air miles from these trips to Australia," Daniel replied. "Why don't we travel together? You have that sabbatical coming up and I'll quit my job. I'm sure there'll be something I can find when we get back."

Emily hugged Daniel and replied, "Let's do it."

Research

The previous chapters tell the story of a failed project being rerun successfully, based on my experience with dozens of engineering teams alongside the scientific research conducted to empirically understand this.

In this chapter, I want to briefly explain the scientific basis for this research.

During my career, I've spent a significant amount of time working on various operational problems, such as in road traffic systems and operations research of various types of engineering teams.

In 2021, I was commissioned to research burnout amongst software engineers. At the time, studies would be conducted using very large "snowball" samples of thousands of software engineers.

With Survation, I pioneered the use of representative opinion polling for this purpose. Survation have a formidable track record when it comes to their opinion polling. They had correctly predicted surprise election results in 2015, 2017, and 2019, alongside predicting the outcomes of both the UK's referendum on European Union membership and the Scottish independence referendum. Survation is a member of the British Polling Council and abides by its rules.

Our July 2021 research found a whopping 83% of UK software engineers had experienced burnout, and when repeated in November 2023, this rate remained steady at 81%.

The use of representative opinion polling allowed us to publish our research quicker than any other research team, including Google's DORA team. When other teams published their results across all the dimensions we measured, our results were consistent.

The results also showed some alarming data about how software engineers' concerns regarding software reliability at their workplace. Specifically, 83% were concerned about software reliability at their workplace, with 20% being concerned "to a great extent". However, this research was conducted before various software scandals like the Post Office Horizon IT Scandal hit headlines in the UK, pushing such issues to the forefront of public perception.

During that time, I also conducted investigations for Haystack to see why some software engineering teams were performing well at continuous improvement while others weren't. The investigations across a significant number of organisations found an almost universal rule that fundamentals were critically important when it came to how well organisations would perform. The universal rule seemed to be that the predictors of success were that the person driving the change was in senior management rather than middle management, that the Chief Technology Officer had at least an undergraduate qualification in a science, technology, engineering, or mathematics (STEM) discipline, and that they had some prior experience in a commercial role. Those organisations who didn't meet these criteria seemed almost impossible to change later on.

Later in November 2023, I also conducted research for the auditing firm Engprax, of which I was the CEO. Our research findings indicated that 53% of software engineers suspected wrongdoing at work, and 75% who reported it would face retaliation. The top reasons people did not report wrongdoing were fear of retaliation from management (59%) and fear of retaliation from colleagues (44%).

Alongside this research, I also began to sample the British public generally on attitudes toward software engineering. We conducted a nationally representative sample of 1,989 British adults, providing 95% confidence the 'true' result will fall within 2.20% of the sample result. At the time, software productivity metrics would favour measures of speed (namely the speed to ship new features and fix bugs). However, the research suggested that getting the latest features as quickly as possible was the least important factor of 10 different dimensions measured. Instead, the public was most likely to agree "to a great extent" that data security (62%), data accuracy (55%), and ensuring there are no serious bugs (55%) mattered to them.

For Haystack, I was then commissioned to investigate what percentage of software projects fail to be delivered on-time, perceptions of on-time delivery amongst business decision makers, and how performance was measured.

Reviewing previous research, I found that approximately 70% of software projects failed to be delivered on-time. Some studies placed the figure as low as 69%, whilst one placed the figure as high as 84%.

The 70% failure rate came despite one study finding that 82.5% of software engineers rated the importance of on-time completion of projects as high or very high.

Next, I commissioned J.L. Partners to poll 500 business decision-makers in the UK and USA on the importance of on-time delivery of software. Like Survation, J.L. Partners is a member of the British Polling Council and abides by its rules.

The results showed 81% of business decision-makers in the UK and 89% in the USA are concerned about on-time delivery of software projects in their organisations. 44% of respondents in the UK and 57% in the USA said they were "very concerned".

Indeed, 93% in the UK and 95% in the USA consider on-time delivery as important when evaluating the performance of software engineering teams, with 63% saying "very important" in the UK and 66% in the USA.

Furthermore, 77% of business decision-makers in the UK and 90% in the USA say on-time delivery is the main way they measure the performance of software engineering teams. 98% in the UK and 96% in the USA agree with the statement, "The goal of a software engineering team is to deliver high-quality software on-time," with 65% in the UK and 62% in the US strongly agreeing.

The result therefore seemed consistent with Haystack's own market research that it wasn't speed of delivery that was important, it was on-time delivery that really mattered – a subtle but important difference.

Finally, the research found that empirical measurement of impact was essential over the use of subjective surveys.

Data collected by Survation showed software engineers often had inflated self-assessment of performance, with 94% of software engineers rating their job performance as average or above. A historical study was consistent with this, finding that software engineers tend to overestimate their performance with up to 42% rating themselves in the top 5%. Men are 26% more likely than women to consider themselves better than average performers.

Additionally, prior research has also shown that "those with the lowest programming skill" are most likely to be most over-optimistic at evaluating software delivery performance in large projects.

Interestingly, this positivity doesn't extend to management – software engineers are nearly 17% more likely on average to agree to a great or moderate extent that other managers in the industry are generally good compared to their own.

The use of subjective measurements also saw other issues. Nearly one in three software engineers (31%) either didn't feel their achievements at work were well-celebrated at all, or only "to a small extent". One in four software engineers said they were unable to take calculated risks without fear of negative consequences.

This psychological safety to take risks and express ideas or concerns is clearly foundational, but it would also become apparent there was something more primitive that was key too.

When I returned to consulting work, I began to see in numerous situations that software failures seemed to come about due to failures in the requirements engineering process, rather than processes later in the software development lifecycle.

In a book I wrote, "How to Protect Yourself from Killer Computers", I reviewed numerous case studies of catastrophic computer failures. These case studies included instances of people being subject to killer radiation overdoses in hospitals, planes entering "death dives", and fatal car crashes.

Regulators and other investigative bodies would often attribute failures to the requirements engineering process. The typical anatomy of a scandal would start with the system being poorly designed to begin with, often with no design documents or specification. This would lead to issues whereby improperly designed requirements would contribute to problems downstream in the actual development and implementation.

From here, the problems would then be covered up, and internal whistleblowers would be ignored or face retaliation as the problems mounted, ultimately snowballing into massive challenges.

In the past, weak requirements were seen as simple poor engineering practice. However, starting development without the most basic requirements has increasingly become a practice justified under Agile software development methodologies. In the case of the Post Office Horizon IT Scandal, there was an explicit decision to adopt an Agile software development methodology (namely Rapid Application Development), which actively promoted this requirements-light approach.

Toyota is often considered as one of the early pioneers of the Agile methodology, with much of the work finding its roots in the Toyota Production

System. After an incident involving a software bug causing fatal car crashes came to light, a 2007 internal Toyota email remarked, "In truth, technology such as failsafe is not part of the Toyota Engineering division's DNA."

The values in the Agile Manifesto are written as follows:

> *Individuals and interactions over processes and tools*
>
> *Working software over comprehensive documentation*
>
> *Customer collaboration over contract negotiation*
>
> *Responding to change over following a plan*

Considering the latter three of these values, I wanted to put these to the test to see how they actually impacted the delivery of software. Are software projects really more successful when they devalue having a documented, upfront plan in favour of shipping software without requirements and changing as needed?

In other words, I wanted to understand for both successful and unsuccessful projects:

1. Were the project requirements clear before the software development process had begun?
2. Did the project have a complete specification or requirements document before the development started?
3. Did engineers have to make significant changes to the requirements late in the development process?

Additionally, I wanted to understand how some other practices impacted software delivery for successful and unsuccessful projects:

4. Were the project requirements accurately based on the real-world problem?
5. Did engineers have to work on more than one project at the same time?
6. Did engineers feel you were able to discuss and address problems quickly when they emerged during the project?

The fourth question is about ensuring the requirements actually are rooted in the problem, rather than a solution in want of a problem. The fifth question is about the impact of minimising work-in-progress, and the sixth is about whether the team is able to address issues when they snowball.

To ensure simplicity, respondents could only answer with a binary yes or no to each of these questions.

To evaluate the split of these practices between projects which are successful and those which are unsuccessful, the respondents would first be asked: "Thinking about the last software project you encountered; was it successfully delivered on-time and on-budget, to a high standard of quality?"

I also wanted to understand how particular methodologies in total affected delivery rates, so I also evaluated the success in the following instances:

1. Where the respondents avoided Agile practices (1=yes, 2=yes, and 3=no).
2. Where the respondents used the Lean approach of only working on one project at a time to minimise work-in-progress (5=no).
3. Where the respondents used the Impact Engineering approach outlined in this book (1=yes, 2=yes, 3=no, 4=yes, 5=either, 6=yes).

The reason why the respondents were asked about practices and not to name the methodology is that many don't actually understand the methodology they're using. Many teams will follow the "ceremonies" of a team using the Scrum flavour of Agile, such as backlog grooming and stand-up meetings, but not actually operate using a truly Agile approach.

I commissioned J.L. Partners to conduct this research amongst software engineers in the UK and USA. We polled 250 software engineers in the UK and 350 in the USA, totalling 600 software engineers. The research was conducted from the 3rd of May 2024 to the 7th May 2024.

J.L. Partners solicited responses from 481 software engineers who last encountered a successful project and 119 who last encountered a failed project, to allow sufficient analysis of both groups.

The results were fairly shocking. This is how individual practices affected software development methodology:

- Projects which had clear requirements before the start of the software development process were 97% more likely to succeed than those which didn't.
- Projects where the engineers surveyed felt they couldn't discuss and address problems

quickly when they emerged saw an 87% higher failure rate.

- When the project requirements were accurately based on a real-world problem, projects were 54% more likely to succeed.
- Projects which had a complete specification or requirements document before the start of the software development process were 50% more likely to succeed than those which didn't.
- Projects where there wasn't a need to make significant changes late into the development process saw a 7% higher success rate.

While these all showed a positive result, there was one surprise.

Interestingly, projects where the person surveyed said they didn't have to engage in task-switching between multiple projects were 3% less likely to succeed than those which didn't. Even when combined with any one other practice or all the other practices which do have a positive effect, the results continued to show a minor negative impact. This is surprising given limiting work-in-progress as much as possible is a key tenet of Lean methodology.

Using a scientific technique known as a t-test, I was able to identify that this difference was not statistically significant. Accordingly, there was no statistically significant difference as to whether there were multiple projects the software engineer was working on.

That said, I did not investigate how different extents of context switching mattered. It is interesting to note that previous Haystack Analytics research in March 2021 on Pull Request data found that 40% context switching seemed ideal when it came to increasing developer speed when measured by cycle time (a metric I am no longer fond of given the discussion earlier on speed vs. on-time delivery).

However, another argument against mandating task switching can be found in the July 2021 research by Survation which showed excessive workload is the leading cause of developer burnout.

It is unclear why task switching doesn't seem to make a difference in project success. Potential explanations for this may well be that the best performing engineers take on more work, requirements engineering work leaves more spare time, or that time saved by good practice leaves more time for side projects. However, these are just speculations.

The final comment I'd make on the topic of task switching is in the past I've seen great value in reducing concurrent work and getting things from work-in-progress to actually getting out the door – it's been a key tool in every successful transformation I've done, but it has its limits. When it's no longer the constraint, it's time to focus elsewhere.

When broken down by methodology, those adopting who simply adopted the Lean methodology approach of limiting work-in-progress saw an 21% failure rate, 7% higher than the study baseline (though this data is not statistically significant as we've discussed). 65% of projects would fail when adopting the Agile Manifesto practices around requirements engineering, a 227% increase over the baseline.

Those who adopted Impact Engineering practices saw a 10% failure rate; in other words, they were 50% less likely to fail than the baseline. They were 85% less likely to fail than those using the Agile Manifesto practices around requirements engineering.

The statistical significance of the study data showing that projects using Impact Engineering practices performed better than all others is so strong that the probability of the finding being incorrect is the equivalent of rolling a number six consecutively six times on a fair six-sided dice, on the first attempt.

For the data showing that projects adopting Agile Manifesto practices were more likely to fail, the probability of it being incorrect is the equivalent of, on the first attempt, rolling a number six consecutively five times on a fair six-sided dice.

To put these findings into perspective, CISQ (the Consortium for IT Software Quality) estimated that in 2020, unsuccessful software developments cost the US economy $260 billion, such that a 54% decrease in failure rate would amount to a $115 billion annual saving.

The UK Office of National Statistics estimates that, of the £49.9bn GBP spent on Research and Development annually in 2022, 12.8% was spent on software expenditure. A 54% decrease of the 70% failing projects would amount to over £2 billion.

Finally, the psychology research I've relied on in this book is from already published scientific material rather than original research I've conducted; however, if you are curious as to its efficacy, I've lost 85kg so far through a scientifically driven weight-loss approach (the first 30kg of which was using just the psychological approaches detailed in the book).

Conclusion

My last book, "How to Protect Yourself from Killer Computers", was a book that I largely wrote for others – primarily created for software engineers yet accessible to a wider audience using plain-English explanations and language.

This book, however, is a book that I wrote for myself in the past, containing insights I wish I'd have known years ago but had to find out myself.

Eliyahu Goldratt's book "The Goal" presented both a continuous improvement methodology (Theory of Constraints) alongside a project management framework (Drum-Buffer-Rope).

In this book, I've sought to do something similar. While Jess is primarily concerned with the psychology of achieving transformation, Daniel was concerned with successfully delivering software on-time.

The psychology of personal transformation and engineering for impact have a symbiotic relationship. Personal transformation can be achieved when we focus on our biggest problems and move to resolve them. Similarly, engineering for impact requires us to understand the problems we truly face and come to a solution.

We are clearly normally not good at either. As described throughout this book, 70% of software projects fail to be delivered on-time and the success rate of transformation initiatives when studied have been found to be in the low single-digit percentages (if not a fraction of a percent).

Agile historically deprioritised the importance of the requirements engineering process in favour of responding to situations in real-time. However, the story told in the book, the case studies I've explored, and the scientific data show that requirements engineering is a fundamentally important process.

When solving a problem, you must first understand the problem. This is done by documenting the requirements of the solution clearly before you begin.

In software engineering, this doesn't mean you need to produce lengthy specifications for the smallest pieces of work – it's just about ensuring that a degree of requirements engineering is done to avoid making significant changes later or solving a problem that doesn't exist.

When I designed the study for this book, I thought I'd be likely to find that task-switching is a major risk when it comes to completing projects on-time.

However, I have not been able to find such evidence in the research (yet). Indeed, the data shows that it does not appear to make a statistically significant difference.

However, the prior research has shown that high workload is a leading cause of burnout, so at least I would hope the advice to avoid taking on too much work is worthwhile. I also think if you identify that excess work-in-progress is your bottleneck, you should by all means fix it, as long as you only optimise it while it's a constraint (and not some false idol).

Another key to success is being able to discuss and address problems quickly when they emerge during a project, and this requires psychological safety within an organisation.

However, it is crucial to prioritise emotions in order for any transformation initiative to be successful. When problems emerge, first attune yourself to the emotions of the person with the problem, and then address the problem.

Some people may seek to solely focus on the emotional aspects, whilst others will solely look to focus on the problem – both are inadequate.

Over recent months, I've been exposed many people who follow these extremes. Those who only focus on appeasing emotions find themselves in snowballing problems and those who solely look to solve the problems will encounter unnecessary resistance.

Be aware of and responsive to the needs of others, but don't lose sight of fixing the problems.

To improve your ability to change, practice your skills in self-belief (but not narcissism), self-motivation, emotional self-regulation, and conscientiousness (meaning responsibility, care, and diligence). At the same time, cultivating gratitude, compassion, and pride can help individuals delay reward gratification and thus persist in tasks.

Finally, it is essential to recognise you cannot force others to change; you can only give them the information, tools, and self-belief they need to achieve their goals.

Techniques Summarised

Impact Engineering steps:

1. Define the problem.
2. Find the solution to the problem.
3. Implement the solution.
4. Analyse to see if the solution meets the requirements.
5. Repeat as required and focus on finishing rather than starting.

Impact Engineering checklist:

1. Have clear requirements before starting the development process.
2. Discuss and address problems quickly when they emerge during the project.
3. Accurately base the requirements on a real-world problem.
4. Document the requirements in a specification or requirements document.
5. Plan well to avoid making significant changes late into the development process.
6. Avoid burnout by not taking on an excessive workload at the same time.

Transformation tips:

1. Recognise you cannot force others to change.
2. Identify your biggest risk and address it.
3. Be wary of loss aversion stopping you killing your demons.
4. Prioritise emotional wellbeing when driving change.
5. To improve your ability to change, practice your skills in self-belief (but not narcissism), self-motivation, emotional self-regulation, and conscientiousness (meaning responsibility, care, and diligence).
6. Gratitude, compassion, and pride encourage people to delay gratification.

Engineering practices by increase in project success when used:

Engineering Practice	Increase (%)
The project requirements were clear before the software development process began	97%
Being able to discuss and address problems quickly (i.e., "psychological safety")	87%
The project requirements were accurately based on the real-world problem	54%
The project had a complete specification or requirements document before the development started	50%
Significant changes were made to the requirements late in the development process	7%
The software engineer reported not having to work on more than one project at the same time	No statistically significant difference.

THE END

Printed in Great Britain
by Amazon